Contents

Teachers' notes

The aim of this book

The aim of this book is to provide varied and stimulating activities, especially suited to pupils with special needs in mainstream classrooms, so that they are able to work within the class at their own level. These activities will supplement any existing scheme of work for mathematics and many of them can be adapted to several ability levels.

Using this book

The activities in this book are organised progressively so teachers may find they get the best results by using them in the order in which they appear. However it is not essential to do this. Prompt cards (see 'Mathematical language' below) and gameboards can be made durable by sticking them on to card and covering them in clear adhesive film. Other equipment made by the pupils, such as dice, can be used as appropriate.

Teacher support

Once the initial instruction on each photocopiable sheet is explained to the pupil, the activities may be attempted independently. Children should be encouraged to talk about their work – asking for help or discussing results, as appropriate. This can be done with any ancillary help available as well as with the teacher.

Mathematical language

Most pupils learn mathematical language with experience and regular exposure to basic signs, symbols and so on. Many children with special needs,

however, do not and require constant prompts to remind them what it all means. To combat this the book features key word lists in the form of 'prompt cards' which can be referred to at any time, but especially when pupils are working on the photocopiable sheets. The language used on the prompt cards has been carefully chosen and kept to a basic minimum (although you may wish to add to the word lists once the idea is established and individual needs increase). They may also be used for reading and writing activities, increasing the child's ability to work independently.

The best way to use these prompt card packs is to access them regularly. Teachers, ancillary helpers, parents and peer partners can all be involved in reinforcing key vocabulary. Before any new photocopiable sheet is attempted, a review of the vocabulary will help pupils read the instructions and follow them successfully, allowing them to feel independent as they complete the work. Thus prompt cards work in three main ways:
- as a repetitive teaching aid;
- as a constant visual prompt to ensure success;
- as an aid towards independent work completion.

Notes on individual activities

Page 5: Prompt cards

This activity introduces the language of instruction that will be used throughout this book. The Instructions prompt card should be cut out, stuck on to card and kept safely. It will be useful for many activities in the book.

Page 6: Words for rules

In this activity the signs +, − and = are introduced, together with the parallel vocabulary. Numbers up to 10 have been chosen to give the pupils a sense of success and achievement from the beginning. The numbers and equations can be extended further depending on the ability levels of individual pupils.

Page 7: Words for numbers

This activity gives practice in recognising matching words and numbers. The words cardinal and ordinal are introduced – these may require teacher instruction to optimise success in the activities which refer to them.
Extension activity: The prompt card can be used for further examples of cardinal and ordinal activities. Since most pupils can count in tens up to 100, the 'Tens' prompt card capitalises on this skill and introduces words for the activities which follow.

Page 8: Wordsearch

Language work done with cardinal and ordinal numbers is consolidated here, by searching for matching words.
Extension activity: Encourage the pupils to use words from one of the prompt cards to make a wordsearch of their own.

Solution:

a	c	t	w	e	n	t	y	d	t
d	e	w	f	g	i	z	s	h	p
k	b	o	q	g	m	r	e	k	j
j	l	m	r	t	e	a	d	c	l
t	e	n	t	h	u	s	s	u	a
e	c	i	h	j	f	i	r	s	t
j	a	d	n	r	k	x	m	g	h
o	n	f	b	t	c	h	b	e	r
f	i	f	t	y	k	d	a	i	e
g	b	s	e	v	e	n	t	y	e

Page 9: Digit cards

Here, digit cards are used to manipulate bigger numbers. Children should aim to work systematically but may need help to get started. These cards have many uses and only a few examples are used on this photocopiable sheet such as counting in tens. Teachers may wish to extend their use with later photocopiable sheets. The digit cards should be cut out, stuck on card and placed in an envelope for safe keeping.

Page 10: Dots on dice

This activity presents a practical session in making and numbering dice (which may need some adult supervision). Games and activities with dice will be revisited so pupils should be encouraged to keep their dice for later use.
Extension activity: Consider introducing different nets of cubes, such as:

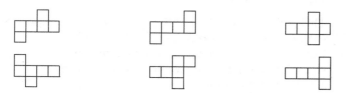

Page 11: Fun with dice

Numbering to 12 is reinforced in these activities which can be played singly, in pairs or in small groups. The dice made earlier (page 10) might be used here. Children should record their throws on the tally chart and should notice that they can only colour the '1' section by throwing a single dice. The last activity on the page asks children to practise cumulative totalling from given clues and can be done many times, with different starting numbers. Ensure the children understand that the dice only provides the starting number and is then no longer required. They could also change the clues on the arrows.
Extension activity: Other tracks can be made by children using their own choice of numbers as clues.

Page 12: Dots on dominoes

This activity reinforces numbering and matching. It requires a full set of dominoes and involves sorting into sets. It can be used as an introduction to algebra. Children will be left with the double blank.
Extension activity: Try extending this by introducing other types of sorting – packs of cards into suits, a class of pupils, types of animals, numbers below 10, above 10 and so on.

Page 13: More dominoes

This activity reinforces dots and number matching. Children will need a full box of dominoes and a ruler marked in inches to use for a number line.
Extension activity: Children could formulate their own alternative equations for each number on the number line to extend their understanding.

Page 14: Dominosearch

These activities extend the matching of dots with numbers, and ordering numbers to 12. A full set of dominoes is required.
Extension activity: Pupils could be given a larger number of dominoes (a maximum of 12) to loop.

Page 15: Ordering numbers

This activity works with numbers from 10–20, matching words with numbers. It introduces prompt card 'Ten to twenty' which may be added to the pack for future reference and help. (See page 9 for making your own digit cards.)
Extension activity: Other number and word matches may be made by the pupil and similar activity sheets could be devised, using greetings cards and catalogues as a source of pictures for counting objects, then recording words for numbers.

Page 16: Comparing numbers

The comparing prompt card introduces vocabulary for making comparisons. Some teacher instruction may be necessary to clarify the words.
Extension activity: The work may be extended by using more 'before' and 'after' exercises.

Page 17: Numbersearch

This activity uses other numbers to practise 'greater than' and 'less than'.
Extension activity: Once numbering up to 50 has been mastered, the 50 square itself can be photocopied and made into a jigsaw.

Page 18: Numbergrid

The children are asked to colour squares on a 50 grid. The shape produced will be the rough outline of a spaceman. Further practice on numbers 'before' and 'after' is also provided.

Page 19: Mars pathfinder

Children are given the instructions for a Mars pathfinder game. These should be discussed before the game is played in pairs. All the clues have been deliberately kept off the gameboard so it can be used for other games. (See also page 32: Treasure Island.)
Extension activity: Children could draw other shapes to create a type of Snakes and Ladders.

Page 20: Odds and evens

This activity introduces children to the concept of odds and evens, taking this skill as far as 20. Initial teacher instruction will greatly enhance the learning that can be gained from this sheet.
Extension activity: The work can be extended to 50 by using this number sequence as a repeating pattern. Children's knowledge will be increased by naming the numbers in the larger sequence. This will prepare them for page 21.

Page 21: Missing numbers

The activities on this page extend the idea of number sequencing to 50. They are intended to add to children's confidence as their success in manipulating numbers is increased.

Page 22: Skyscrapers

Pupils are required to practise their skills of recognising number sequences and patterns in order to find missing numbers. Each vertical window pattern in the skyscrapers has a sequence number missing, which the child must find. All the numbers involved are below 50. The last activity formalises these skills and can be extended to many other examples.

Pages 23 and 24: Making two-times patterns and Making three-times patterns

These activities aim to increase children's understanding of the concept of multiplication. Once both photocopiable sheets have been completed some teacher instruction will help to consolidate and emphasise the idea of $3 \times 2 = 2 \times 3$. This establishes a new pattern concept which will be extended later (see pages 31 and 32). The dot-to-dot on page 23 should reveal a car.

Page 25: Wheels and whirlys

This activity consolidates work on the two- and three-times tables. It can also be used for addition and subtraction if the numbers and signs on the vehicles are changed. Alternatively easier addition and subtraction clues might be used. The game could be practised with the 20 square initially to lead up to this more demanding consolidation of ×2 and ×3 with the 30 square, although in this case not all numbers would be covered.

Page 26: Rally racers

The numbering system is taken to 100 as children solve multiplication equations on selected numbers. The game offers multiplication clues which help the player to move along rapidly. Initially it should be played in pairs but, as the pupils become more adept, it can be extended for use with small groups. Clues on the numbers can be replaced by others to extend skills and game use for differing ability levels (+/− clues may be used as reinforcement). Children should check answers with their prompt cards.

Page 27: Counting to 100

This activity reinforces numbering to 100. It introduces a 100 square through sequential counting. The word problems revisit vocabulary introduced earlier, so reinforcing understanding.
Extension activity: This can be extended into a game for pairs with one child making up new word problems for a partner to solve.

Page 28: Fun with 100

The idea of pattern in number sequences is reinforced by this activity which increases children's ability to deal with numbers up to 100. The photocopiable sheet reviews the two- and three-times tables as well as counting in fives and tens. The prompt cards from pages 23 and 24 may be useful. The lorry-loading activity helps children to recognise and focus on the particular skill required to solve practical problems. Children should notice that 90 may be joined to more than one lorry.

Page 29: 100 square gameboard

Children will enjoy devising their own games. This 100 square gameboard has the numbers appearing in a right to left, then left to right sequence. Discuss this with the children first, then give them several photocopies of the sheet and provide opportunities for them to discuss with a teacher, helper or friend how their games will work. Use the gameboard also for Treasure Island (page 32).

Page 30: Crack the code

This activity challenges children to develop problem-solving skills by cracking codes. The teacher will need to introduce the storyline and give some instruction in code systems.

Sam's messages read:

A Help

B Treasure here

C Don't tell anyone

Asif replies:

D Help coming

E Don't worry

F Bringing big sack

Extension activity: Other messages could be attempted. Help may be needed for this.

Page 31: Share the treasure

This activity gives practice in balancing equations, taking the skills of addition, subtraction and multiplication in turn. Children may need some support initially to see how the balancing works.

Extension: Children could extend the activity by choosing other types and amounts of treasure and balancing it equally.

Page 32: Treasure Island

The work done on equations is reviewed here. Children might use the 50 square (page 19) or 100 square gameboard (page 29) for this activity. The clues should include addition and subtraction as well as simple multiplication by 2, 3, 5 and 10. Children may need help to devise the clues and get the game started. Once underway they should be able to continue until all the treasure has been located. Prompt cards could be used to check answers. If challenging a friend, a photocopy of the original map will be required.

Prompt cards

◆ Read the words.
They are all **action words** to help you with your work.
Now try using them.

You will need: a pen or pencil, scissors, glue, some blank card.

Write one word from the prompt card on each line, like this:

read

Then draw the picture underneath each one.

◆ Cut out the prompt card.
Stick it on to card. You will make more prompt cards so keep it safe. It is the first card in your **prompt pack**.

This is a **prompt card**.

Instructions

read
write
draw
colour
cut
stick
ask
talk
complete

◆ Name _____

Words for rules

◆ Read the words that match each sign on the prompt card at the bottom of this page.

◆ Write the words for:

+ addition   _____   _____   _____

− subtraction   _____   _____   _____

= answer   _____   _____   _____

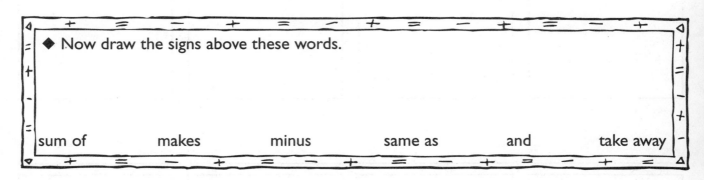

◆ Now draw the signs above these words.

sum of   makes   minus   same as   and   take away

◆ Put in the correct signs to finish these sums.

3 _____ 4 = 7   5 _____ 1 = 4   5 + 5 _____ 10

6 _____ 2 = 4   8 _____ 4 = 4   7 − 3 _____ 4

◆ Answer these:

What is the sum of 1 + 2 + 3 _____

Subtract 1 from 4   _____

6 minus 3 equals   _____

◆ Now cut out the prompt card and stick it on to card. Keep it safe.

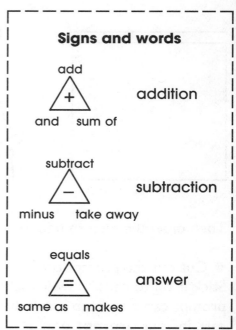

Signs and words

add

$\triangle$ +

and   sum of

addition

subtract

$\triangle$ −

minus   take away

subtraction

equals

$\triangle$ =

same as   makes

answer

◆ Name _____

Words for numbers

◆ Write these cardinal numbers as words:

2 _____   6 _____

3 _____   8 _____   9 _____

◆ Write these ordinal numbers in the right order:

5th   2nd   3rd   1st   4th

_____   _____   _____   _____   _____

◆ Draw three people in a race.
Show who is 1st, 2nd and 3rd.

◆ Read these words:

Cardinal		Ordinal	
0	zero		
1	one	1st	first
2	two	2nd	second
3	three	3rd	third
4	four	4th	fourth
5	five	5th	fifth
6	six	6th	sixth
7	seven	7th	seventh
8	eight	8th	eighth
9	nine	9th	ninth

◆ Write these words as numbers:

twenty _____   eighty _____

fifty _____   a hundred _____

Tens

10	ten
20	twenty
30	thirty
40	forty
50	fifty
60	sixty
70	seventy
80	eighty
90	ninety
100	a hundred

◆ Join each word to the right number:

90   3   7

seven   three

forty   40   ninety

◆ Cut out the prompt cards and stick them on to card.

Wordsearch

You will need: a pen or pencil, a ruler.

a	c	t	w	e	n	t	y	d	b
d	e	w	f	g	i	z	s	h	p
k	b	o	q	g	n	r	e	k	j
j	l	m	r	t	e	a	d	c	l
t	e	n	t	h	u	s	s	u	a
e	c	i	h	i	f	i	r	s	t
j	a	d	n	r	k	x	m	g	h
o	n	f	b	t	c	h	b	e	r
f	i	f	t	y	k	d	a	i	e
g	b	s	e	v	e	n	t	y	e

◆ Find these ten words in the box.

twenty	six	nine	three	tenth
fifty	two	thirty	first	seventy

They may be written across or down.
Draw a line through each one as you find it.

Digit cards

◆ Cut out the digit cards at the bottom of the page.

You will need: a pen or pencil, scissors.

◆ You can put any two numbers together.

Write all the numbers you can make in this box.

◆ What is the biggest number you made? _____

◆ What number is the smallest? _____

◆ Write all the numbers that have 0 in them.

_____   _____   _____

_____   _____   _____

_____   _____   _____

Digit cards

0	1	2	3	4
5	6	7	8	9

Dots on dice

Here is a dice.
It is cube-shaped.

You will need:
a pencil, a ruler,
scissors, glue,
card.

◆ Draw some other cube-shaped things.

The opposite sides of a dice always add up to 7, like this:

:: + • = 7   ::• + •. = 7

If a cube is opened
out it looks like this.
This is called a 'net'.

Try these:

:: + _____ = 7   •. + _____ = 7

•. + _____ = 7   • + _____ = 7

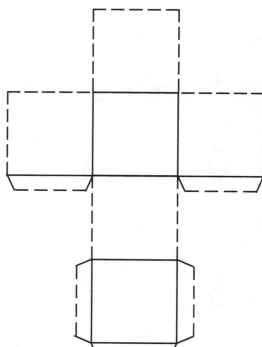

◆ Cut out the net of the cube.
Fold along the lines and stick down the flaps.

◆ Ask for help if you need it.

◆ Draw the dots on each face of the cube.
Remember that opposite sides add up to 7!

◆ Make a second dice.

◆ Keep both your dice to use when you are playing games.

◆ Name _____

Fun with dice

◆ Throw the two dice at the same time.

◆ Add the numbers together. 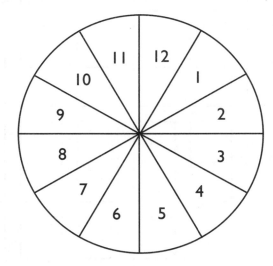 + □ = 7

◆ Colour in the matching number on the clock face.

You will need: a pencil, two dice, coloured pencils, a counter.

Tally chart

1	
2	
3	
4	
5	
6	
7	
8	
9	
10	
11	
12	

◆ Record your total throw each time on the chart.

◆ How many throws did it take to colour all the numbers? _____

◆ Which total did you throw most often? _____

◆ Is there a problem colouring the whole clock face? _____

◆ How will you get round this? _____

◆ Throw one dice and write the number you throw in the start bubble.
Follow the arrows, writing each answer in the next circle.

◆ Name _____

Dots on dominoes

You will need: a pencil, a full box of dominoes.

◆ Set out all the dominoes
so the numbers are showing.

◆ Pick out any dominoes which
have the same number of dots top
and bottom. These are called
doubles. Lay them out like this,
then try to find all the patterns.

◆ Draw the dots on these dominoes.

Find the • • • patterns.

Find the • • • patterns.

Find the • • • patterns.

Find the • • patterns.

Find the • patterns.

Find the • patterns.

◆ Draw the domino
you have left.

◆ Fill in the missing dots in this game of dominoes.
Start from the middle and work to one end, then go back to the middle and work the other way.

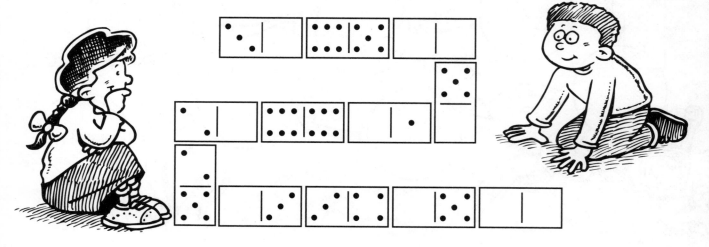

More dominoes

◆ Take out all the dominoes which have blanks on them.

You will need: a pencil, a set of dominoes, a ruler.

◆ Sort the rest into:
- both sides with 6, 4 or 2 dots (even)
- both sides with 1, 3 or 5 dots (odd)
- one side even, one side odd.

◆ Draw in the missing dots on the dominoes below:

One side 6, 4 or 2
One side 1, 3 or 5
even and odd

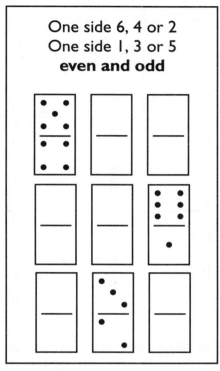

Both sides 6, 4 or 2
even

Both sides 1, 3 or 5
odd

Use a ruler as a number line.

◆ Match one domino to each number as shown below. Make sure the dots on the domino add up to the number.

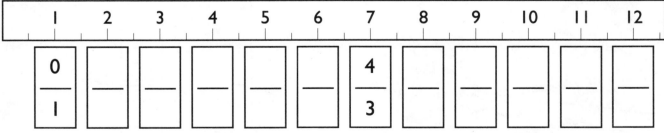

	1	2	3	4	5	6	7	8	9	10	11	12

0						4					
1						3					

◆ Now change the dots to numbers and write them in the blank dominoes.

◆ Finish these:

12 = _____ + _____   9 = _____ + _____   7 = _____ + _____

6 = _____ + _____   10 = _____ + _____   8 = _____ + _____

Dominosearch

◆ Find the dominoes that make up this grid.
Fit them so the numbers match the dots.
Then put them back in the box.

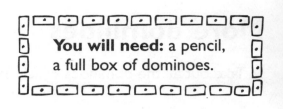

You will need: a pencil,
a full box of dominoes.

6	3		3	4
6	3		3	1
2	5		5	1

◆ Now take out these six dominoes.

◆ Put them together, matching the numbers,
to make a loop like this:

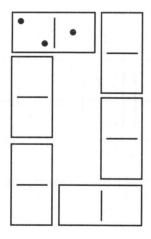

◆ Make another loop using different dominoes.

◆ Talk to a teacher or a friend about what you did.

◆ Name _____

Ordering numbers

You will need: a pencil, scissors, glue, card, digit cards.

◆ Read these numbers and words.

◆ Make the numbers with your digit cards.

◆ Make new double digit cards with the numbers from 10 to 20.

◆ Write the word name for each number on the back, like this:

| 10 | ten |

◆ Write the number and word that matches each picture.

Ten to twenty

10 ten
11 eleven
12 twelve
13 thirteen
14 fourteen
15 fifteen
16 sixteen
17 seventeen
18 eighteen
19 nineteen
20 twenty

◆ Now cut out the prompt card and stick it on to card. Keep it safe.

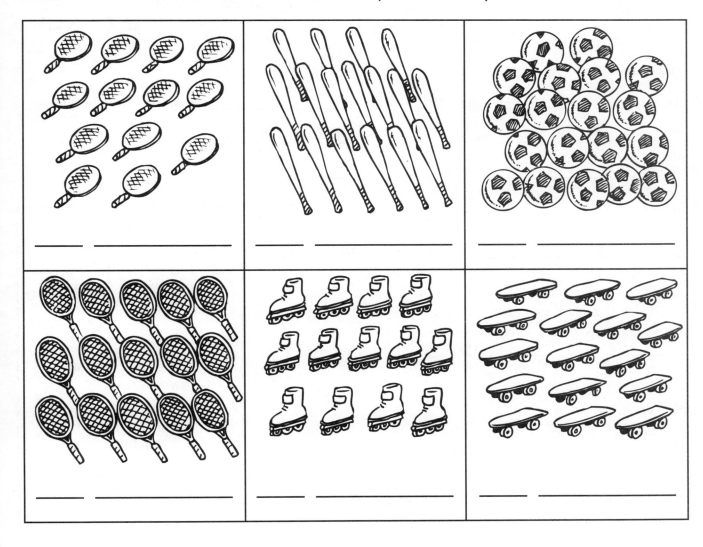

◆ Name _____

Comparing numbers

You will need: a pencil, scissors, glue.

◆ Read these words.

◆ Look at these:

this group of worms

 is bigger than
greater this one

\>

 is smaller than
less this one

\<

3 is the number before 4.   5 is the number after 4.

1 is <u>smaller</u> than 9
<u>less</u>
<u><</u>

16 is <u>greater</u> than 12
<u>more</u>
<u>></u>

Now do these:

14 is _____ than 19   7 is _____ than 4

_____   _____

_____   _____

◆ Write < or > between these pairs of numbers:

2 _____ 8   3 _____ 2   15 _____ 20

◆ Write the number before

_____ 6   _____ 12

◆ Write the number after

7 _____   15 _____

◆ Now cut out the prompt card and stick it on to card.
Keep it safe.

Comparing

bigger
greater } than
more

smaller
less } than
fewer

> is greater than
< is less than

before
after

◆ Name _____

Numbersearch

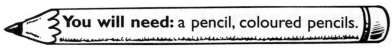

◆ Point to the numbers on the grid as you count to 50.

1	2	3	4	5	6	7	8	9	10
11	12	13	14	15	16	17	18	19	20
21	22	23	24	25	26	27	28	29	30
31	32	33	34	35	36	37	38	39	40
41	42	43	44	45	46	47	48	49	50

Jigsaw pieces:

3
13
23

6
16

24 25 26

7
17
27 28

36 37
46

33 34
41 42 43

39 40
48 49

1 2
11

19 20
29

◆ Colour one of the jigsaw pieces.

◆ Find where it will fit on the grid and colour those squares in the same colour.

◆ Do the same with all the jigsaw pieces. Use a different colour for each one.

◆ Which number is:

2 greater than 16? _____   4 less than 19? _____

3 greater than 34? _____   6 less than 20? _____

4 greater than 40? _____   5 less than 40? _____

◆ Write the answers on the lines.

◆ Name _____

Numbergrid

You will need: coloured pencils.

10	20	30	40	50
9	19	29	39	49
8	18	28	38	48
7	17	27	37	47
6	16	26	36	46
5	15	25	35	45
4	14	24	34	44
3	13	23	33	43
2	12	22	32	42
1	11	21	31	41

◆ Colour these numbers on the grid:

```
                30
        18      29      38
        15      28      35
8       14      27      34      48
7       13      26      33      47
6       12      25      32      46
1       11      24      31      41
```

◆ What shape have you coloured in?

◆ Write the numbers before and after each of these.

For example:

___4___ 5 ___6___   _____ 16 _____   _____ 37 _____

_____ 8 _____   _____ 25 _____   _____ 41 _____

_____ 12 _____   _____ 32 _____   _____ 49 _____

◆ Name _____

Mars pathfinder

◆ Play the Mars pathfinder game with a friend.
You will need a counter each.
See who can get to Mars first.

MARS

Run out of fuel.
Return to Earth (1).

Locked in orbit!
Miss a turn.

41	41	43	44	45	46	47	48	49	☀
40	39	38	37	36	35	34	33	32	31
21	22	23	24	25	26	27	28	29	30
20	19	18	17	16	15	14	13	12	11
1	2	3	4	5	6	7	8	9	10

EARTH

Going well!
Zoom on to 16.

Got up speed!
Zoom on to 32.

Hit by asteroid.
Miss a turn.

◆ Start at 1 (Earth). Take turns to throw the dice. Move your counter the same number of squares as you have thrown. If you land on a square with extra instructions, follow these.

◆ Keep this gameboard to play other games.

Odds and evens

◆ Help the postman by filling in the missing numbers.

◆ Write the complete number sequence for:

Green Street _____ _____ _____ _____ _____

_____ _____ _____ _____ _____

Red Road _____ _____ _____ _____ _____ _____ _____ _____ _____

_____ _____ _____ _____ _____ _____ _____ _____ _____ _____

◆ Mark [odd] and (even) numbers on the number line below, like this:

[1] (2) [3] (4) 5 6 7 8 9 10 11 12 13 14 15 16 17 18 19 20

◆ Name _____

Missing numbers

◆ Fill in the missing number on each line.

2 | 4 | 6 | 8 |

10 | 12 | 14 | 18 | 20

40 | 42 | | 46 | 48

39 | | 35 | 33 | 31

20 | 22 | | 26 | 28

18 | | 14 | 12 | 10

1 | 3 | | 7 | 9

10 | 20 | 30

Skyscrapers

◆ Look at these skyscrapers.

◆ Fill in the missing numbers.

> **You will need:**
> a pencil.

◆ Write the next number in each pattern:

16,   18,   20,   22,   24,   _____

11,   22,   33,   _____

43,   46,   49,   _____

10,   20,   30,   40,   _____

Making two-times patterns

2222222222222222222222222222222222
You will need: coloured
pencils, scissors, glue, card.
2222222222222222222222222222222222

◆ Colour in the even squares, starting with 2.

1	2	3	4	5	6	7	8	9	10
11	12	13	14	15	16	17	18	19	20

Even numbers make up your two-times table.

◆ Complete the list on the prompt card below.

◆ How many 2s make   10? _____   14? _____   20? _____

$11 \times 2 =$ _____ $12 \times 2 =$ _____

◆ Join the dots.
Begin with 2.
End at 24.

◆ What have you drawn?

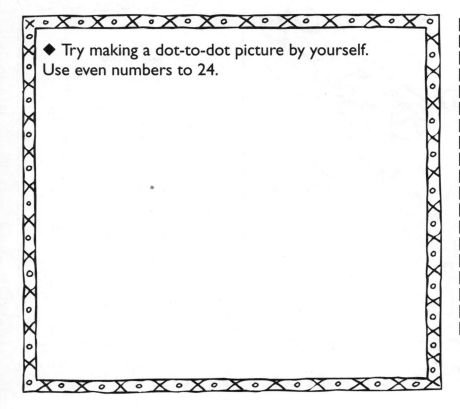

◆ Try making a dot-to-dot picture by yourself.
Use even numbers to 24.

2× table

1	× 2	=	2
2	× 2	=	4
3	× 2	=	6
4	× 2	=	
5	× 2	=	
6	× 2	=	
7	× 2	=	
8	× 2	=	
9	× 2	=	
10	× 2	=	

◆ Cut out the prompt card and
stick it on to card. Keep it safe.

◆ Name _____

Making three-times patterns

◆ Starting at 3, colour in every third square.

1	2	3	4	5	6	7	8	9	10
11	12	13	14	15	16	17	18	19	20
21	22	23	24	25	26	27	28	29	30

◆ Complete the list on the prompt card below.

◆ How many 3s make   15? _____

24? _____

30? _____

11 × 3 = _____   12 × 3 = _____

3x table

1 × 3	=	3
2 × 3	=	6
3 × 3	=	9
4 × 3	=	
5 × 3	=	
6 × 3	=	
7 × 3	=	
8 × 3	=	
9 × 3	=	
10 × 3	=	

◆ Cut out the prompt card and
stick it on to card. Keep it safe.

Wheels and whirlys

You will need: counters, two or more friends, the grid from page 24.

How to play:
Two or more players have a vehicle card each. The caller says a number on the 30 grid and covers it with a counter.
Look at the vehicles on your card and work out the answers.
If one of the answers is the number called, cover it with a counter.
The first one to cover all the pictures is the winner!

◆ Use the grid from page 24 and these cards to play Wheels and whirlys. There are enough cards for four to play. The caller does not have a card.

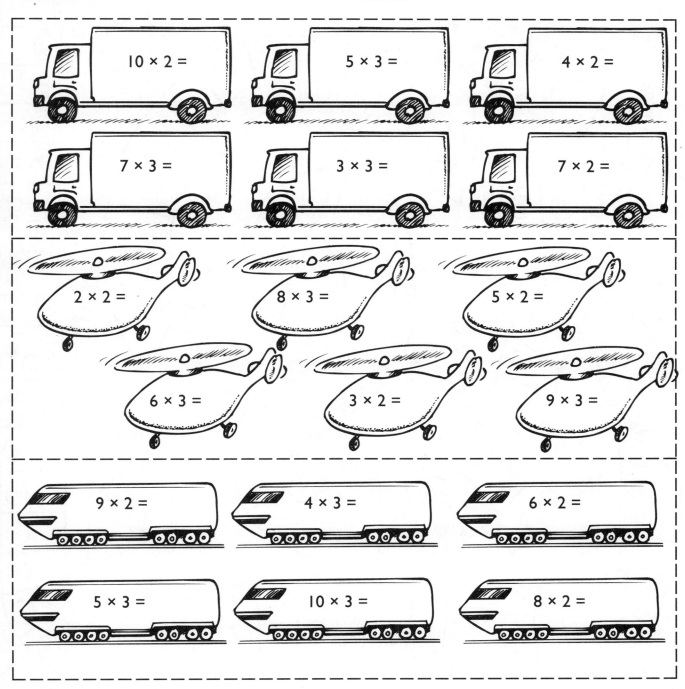

10 × 2 =	5 × 3 =	4 × 2 =
7 × 3 =	3 × 3 =	7 × 2 =
2 × 2 =	8 × 3 =	5 × 2 =
6 × 3 =	3 × 2 =	9 × 3 =
9 × 2 =	4 × 3 =	6 × 2 =
5 × 3 =	10 × 3 =	8 × 2 =

◆ Name _____

Rally racers

How to play: Take turns to throw the dice. Move that number of squares. If you land on a square with a times question on it (such as 4 × 2 = ?) work out the answer and move that number of squares. The first player to reach 100 is the winner.

You will need: a dice, a counter for each player.

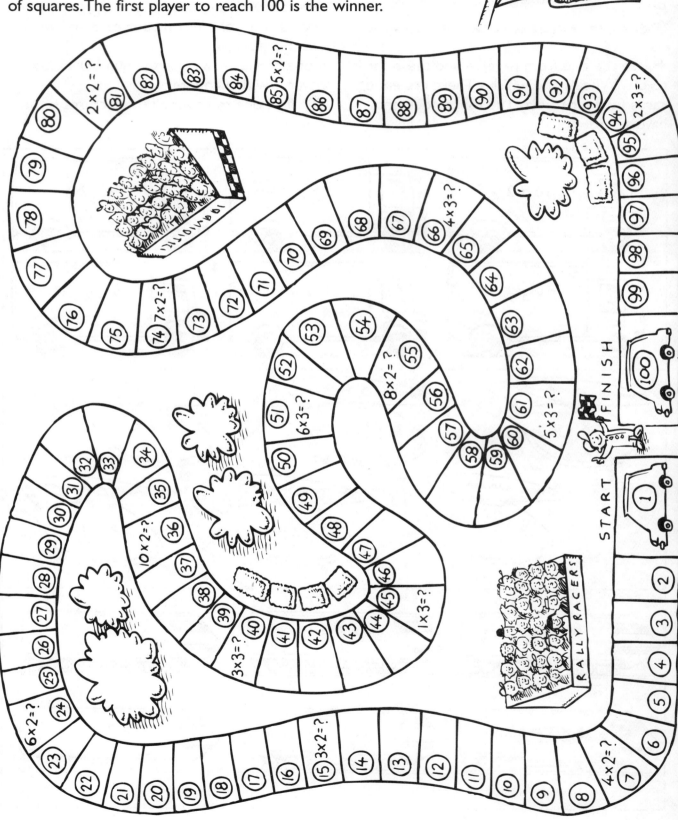

◆ Name _____

Counting to 100

You will need: a pencil.

◆ Count to 100 on this square. Fill in the missing numbers.

1	2	3	4	5	6		8	9	10
11	12		14		16	17	18	19	20
21	22	23	24	25	26	27	28		30
	32	33		35	36		38	39	40
41	42	43	44	45	46	47		49	50
51		53	54	55		57	58	59	
61	62	63		65	66	67	68	69	70
	72		74		76		78	79	
81		83	84	85		87	88		90
91	92		94	95	96	97		99	100

◆ Now use your 100 square to find these numbers.
Write each one on the line, like this:

Three and six make   _____9_____

Nine and two make   _____

Seventeen   _____

One less than 57   _____

The second number after 3   _____

One more than sixty   _____

Two less than 10   _____

Fifty-one   _____

The fourth number after 30   _____

Twenty minus one   _____

Two greater than 29   _____

For working out

Fun with 100

odd	even	odd	even	odd	even	odd	even	odd	even
1	2	3	4	5	6	7	8	9	10
11	12	13	14	15	16	17	18	19	20
21	22	23	24	25	26	27	28	29	30
31	32	33	34	35	36	37	38	39	40
41	42	43	44	45	46	47	48	49	50
51	52	53	54	55	56	57	58	59	60
61	62	63	64	65	66	67	68	69	70
71	72	73	74	75	76	77	78	79	80
81	82	83	84	85	86	87	88	89	90
91	92	93	94	95	96	97	98	99	100

You will need: a pencil, three coloured pencils (red, blue and yellow).

Colour:
the pattern of 2 in yellow,
the pattern of 3 in blue,
the pattern of 5 in red,
all the way up to 100.

(Some squares will have more than one colour!)

◆ Write the pattern of 10

<u>10</u> ____ ____ ____ ____ ____ ____ ____ ____ ____

◆ Join each load to its lorry like this:

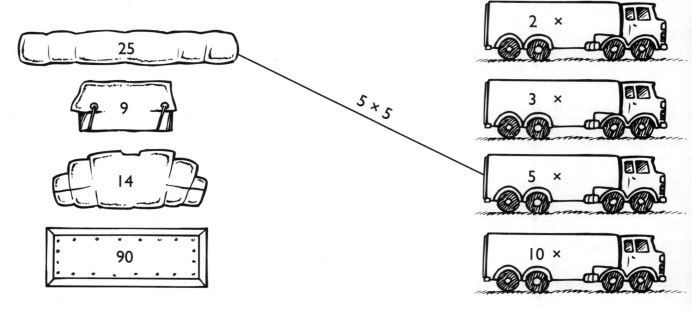

◆ Name _____

100 square gameboard

WINNER

100	99	98	97	96	95	94	93	92	91
81	82	83	84	85	86	87	88	89	90
80	79	78	77	76	75	74	73	72	71
61	62	63	64	65	66	67	68	69	70
60	59	58	57	56	55	54	53	52	51
41	42	43	44	45	46	47	48	49	50
40	39	38	37	36	35	34	33	32	31
21	22	23	24	25	26	27	28	29	30
20	19	18	17	16	15	14	13	12	11
1	2	3	4	5	6	7	8	9	10

◆ With a friend, make up a game to play on this board.

◆ Begin at 1. Move along each line to reach 100.

◆ Can you find ways to make the game more exciting?

Enjoy your games!

◆ Try clues like this:

32: go on 3 places	55: go back to 50	91: miss a turn

◆ Name _____

Crack the code

You will need: a pencil.

Sam the pirate has landed on a treasure island.
He needs help.
He sends messages in bottles to his friend, Asif.
They are in code.

Can you crack the code? This will help you:

1	2	3	4	5	6	7	8	9	10	11	12	13
A	B	C	D	E	F	G	H	I	J	K	L	M

14	15	16	17	18	19	20	21	22	23	24	25	26
N	O	P	Q	R	S	T	U	V	W	X	Y	Z

8 5 12 16

A _____

20 18 5 1 19 21 18 5
8 5 18 5

B _____

_____

4 15 14 20
20 5 12 12
1 14 25 15 14 5

C _____

_____

_____

Asif has found the bottles.
He sends messages back to Sam. What do they say?

8 5 12 16
3 15 13 9 14 7

D _____

_____

4 15 14 20
23 15 18 18 25

E _____

_____

2 18 9 14 7 9 14 7
2 9 7
19 1 3 11

F _____

_____ _____

◆ Send messages of your own in the same code.

◆ Give them to a friend to read.

◆ Think of another way of writing in code.

◆ Try using it in messages.

◆ Name _____

Share the treasure

◆ Sam and Asif want to share the treasure so that they get the same, like this:

$5 + 5 =$ ___7___ + ___3___

$10 + 5 =$ _____ + _____

$11 + 3 =$ _____ + _____

$12 + 7 =$ _____ + _____

$6 - 3 =$ ___10___ – ___7___

$17 - 5 =$ _____ – _____

$19 - 1 =$ _____ – _____

$20 - 10 =$ _____ – _____

_____ $× 5 = 30$

_____ $× 5 = 45$

_____ $× 10 = 50$

_____ $× 10 = 100$

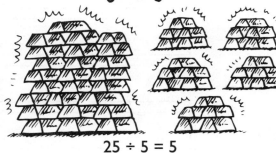

$25 ÷ 5 = 5$

$40 ÷ 5 =$ _____

$60 ÷ 5 =$ _____

$80 ÷ 10 =$ _____

$90 ÷ 10 =$ _____

◆ Choose another treasure. Draw it. Then share it out.

Treasure	Sam's share	Asif's share

◆ Name _____

Treasure Island

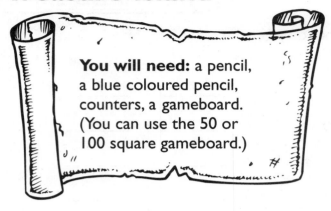

You will need: a pencil, a blue coloured pencil, counters, a gameboard. (You can use the 50 or 100 square gameboard.)

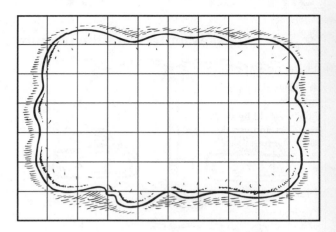

◆ Draw a big island on the gameboard, like this:

◆ Colour the sea all round it. You will not use the blue squares.

◆ Draw each of these treasures in different squares on the island.

coins

rings

necklaces

gold bars

◆ Choose one more, and draw it in too.

◆ In which square did you put the coins?   _____

Clues

rings?   _____

necklaces?   _____

gold bars?   _____

your treasure?   _____

◆ Make a clue next to the number, like this: _____25_____ | 5 × 5 |

◆ Play this game with a friend who has a copy of your map and the clues.

◆ Take turns to ask your clues.

◆ Put a counter on each treasure as you find it.

◆ Did you find all the treasure?